SHAPED SUPER COLOURING FUN

RAINBOW PRINCESSES

This book belongs to

SHAPED SUPER COLOURING FUN RAINBOW PRINCESSES

A LAUGHING LOBSTER BOOK 978-1-910765-44-9
Published in Great Britain by Laughing Lobster
an imprint of Centum Publishing Ltd.
This edition published 2021.
1 3 5 7 9 10 8 6 4 2

Illustrations by Charlotte Archer.

Laughing Lobster an imprint of Centum Publishing Ltd, 20 Devon Square,
Newton Abbot, Devon, TQ12 2HR, UK

books@centumpublishingltd.co.uk

LAUGHING LOBSTER AN IMPRINT OF CENTUM
PUBLISHING LIMITED. Reg. No. 08497203

A CIP catalogue record for this book is available
from the British Library.

Printed in China.

Add some rainbow brights to this happy princess and her **castle**.

When you spot a **princess** colour her in. There are **5** to find.

Colour in this **royal horse** and then give him or her a name.

Write it here:

Add pretty patterns and bright colours to these princesses' **dresses.**

Make these crowns sparkle with all the colours of the **rainbow**.

Doodle in some patterns and **dazzling** gems too.

Can you spot **8 differences** between these pictures?

When you're done, colour them in.

Add some bling-tastic colours to all the jewels and gems.

Doodle in the details on this **royal carriage** and add some rainbow colours.

Give these princesses
some **dazzling** hairstyles.

This princess wants long flowing locks.

Doodle a ballerina bun
for this princess.

Create a pretty
ponytail or plait
for this smiling
princess.

Use your colours to give these
princesses two **dreamy** ballgowns.

Colour in all the clothes and accessories to help this princess tidy up her bedroom.

Add some **rainbow** colours to this princess.

Keep colouring till you've
transformed these princesses with
all the colours of the **rainbow**.

Colour in these pictures
to create some **stylish**
accessories for this princess.

Colour in these pictures with your favourite colours.

Colour in
all the hearts
to show how much you
love
princesses.

This princess and her magical unicorn need some dazzling colours to make them **shine**.

This princess is having her first **sleepover party**. Draw some princess friends to join in the fun.

Copy these princesses into the grids, then colour all the pictures in.

Trace over the lines and add some colour to complete the **castle**.

Use your colours to give this princess the best **birthday party** ever!

The princess
loves
to play with her
little friends.

Join the dots to
finish off this princess'
favourite pet.

Add some pretty colours to the royal **carriage**.

Make these flowers
bloom
with your
brightest colours.

Join the **dots** and add some colour to this picture.

When the flags are flying
it means the **princesses**
are at home.

Choose some different colours for
each princess to **transform** their hair.

Colour in the picture to help this princess get ready for bed. **Sweet dreams!**

Colour in this last page
so the princesses live

HAPPILY
EVER
AFTER!